HIRAGANA
GAMBATTE!

HIRAGANA

■■■■■ ひらがながんばって！ ■■■■■

GAMBATTE!

Deleece Batt

Kodansha International
Tokyo · New York · London

Distributed in the United States by Kodansha America, Inc., 114, Fifth Avenue, New York, New York 10011, and in the United Kingdom and continental Europe by Kodansha Europe Ltd., 95 Aldwych, London WC2B 4JF. Published by Kodansha International Ltd., 17-14, Otowa 1-chome, Bunkyo-ku, Tokyo 112 and Kodansha America Inc.

First edition, 1993
93 94 95 96 10 9 8 7 6 5 4 3 2 1

ISBN 4-7700-1797-9

Designed by Adachi Office
Set in Times, *Kyokashotai*, *Goshikkutai* and *Minchotai* on a Macintosh
Printed in Japan by Dai-Nippon Printing Company

Library of Congress cataloging in publication data available

CONTENTS

Rationale

Hiragana Gambatte! recommends an approach to teaching Japanese based on the eight teaching and learning principles in the *Australian Language Levels (ALL) Guidelines.*

Learners learn a language best when:

1. They are treated as individuals with their own needs and interests;
2. They are provided with opportunities to participate in communicative use of the Japanese language in a wide range of activities;
3. They are exposed to communicative data which is comprehensible and relevant to their own needs and interests;
4. They focus deliberately on various language forms, skills and strategies in order to support the process of language acquisition;
5. They are exposed to sociocultural data and direct experience of the culture embedded within the Japanese language;
6. They become aware of the role and nature of language and culture;
7. They are provided with appropriate feedback about their process;
8. They are provided with opportunities to manage their own learning.

Vale, D. et al. (1991) *Pocket ALL*, Curriculum Corporation, Melbourne.

Preface

Japanese scripts—*hiragana*, *katakana* and *kanji*—offer an exciting challenge for many people worldwide yet are still considered by some to be too difficult to master. *Hiragana Gambatte!* introduces *hiragana* through visual association with a familiar word or concept, encouraging the learning of *hiragana* as soon as the study of the language begins.

While I was a project writer with the National Japanese Curriculum in Australia, teachers often expressed their dilemma of how and when to introduce *hiragana*. I advocate that regardless of age, students should be introduced to script as soon as they start learning Japanese. Postponing the introduction of *hiragana* in favour of *romaji* only delays the mastering of script. *Hiragana Gambatte!* provides correct stroke order to follow and adequate practice space.

The importance of culture being taught as part of language cannot be underestimated and *Hiragana Gambatte!* provides students with informative authentic culture notes illustrated to enthrall and delight. Students can become involved with some of the interesting activities associated with some of the culture notes or use the information to celebrate special days.

As a resource for schools or home study, *Hiragana Gambatte!* compliments both the National Japanese Curriculum in Australia and other universal Japanese language programs.

To all my colleagues in Japan and Australia, for their informed contributions, their key role is greatly acknowledged. I also wish to thank my husband Gerard and son Dalton for their enthusiasm and inspiration.

Deleece Batt
B.A. (M.A.S) Dip.Ed.
1993

THE JAPANESE WRITING SYSTEM

CALLIGRAPHY

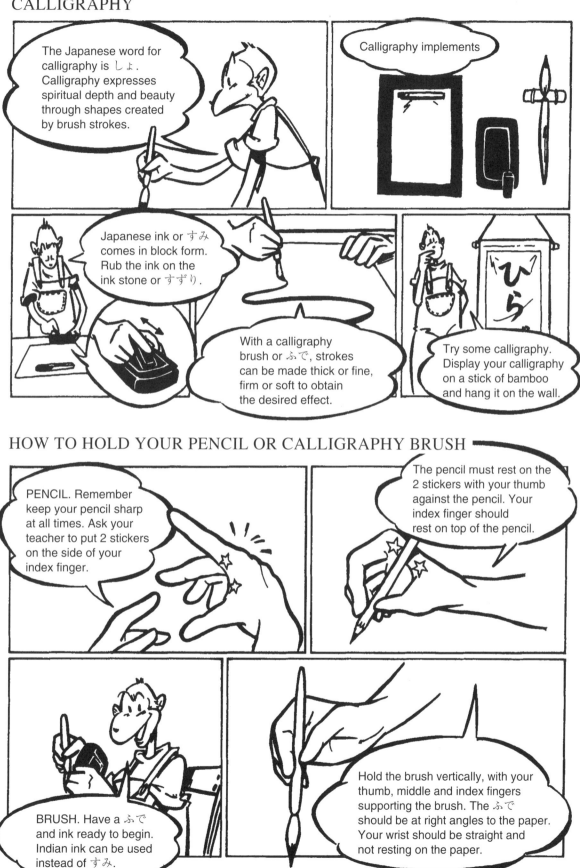

HOW TO HOLD YOUR PENCIL OR CALLIGRAPHY BRUSH

9

SIMPLE HIRAGANA CHART

The hiragana chart on the next page shows the forty-six hiragana characters. In this workbook you will learn how to recognize and write all forty-six hiragana. Once you have completed the hiragana practice section you will be able to practise writing Japanese words at the bottom of each page. Remember to show your work to your teacher before you continue.

あ a	い i	う u	え e	お o
か ka	き ki	く ku	け ke	こ ko
さ sa	し shi	す su	せ se	そ so
た ta	ち chi	つ tsu	て te	と to
な na	に ni	ぬ nu	ね ne	の no
は ha	ひ hi	ふ fu	へ he	ほ ho
ま ma	み mi	む mu	め me	も mo
や ya	（い）	ゆ yu	（え）	よ yo
ら ra	り ri	る ru	れ re	ろ ro
わ wa	（い）	（う）	（え）	を o
ん n				

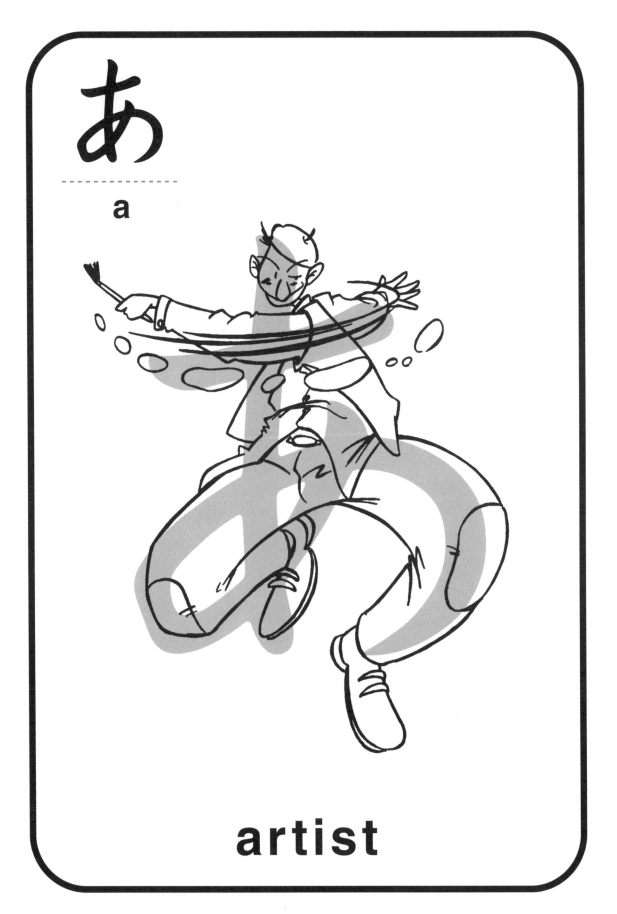

あ

a

artist

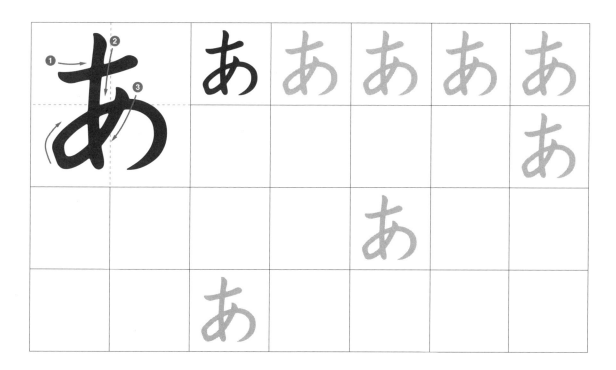

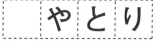

	い	き	ど	う

	や	と	り

あいきどう is a popular Japanese art of self-defence that requires little physical strength and no weapons. A series of locks and holds are used to cause an opponent's own strength to work against him. Can you imagine using Schwarzenegger's strength against him?

あやとり is a game like cat's cradle in which you make shapes from a loop of string that you hold and twist between your fingers. With some practice, maybe you could pull a couple loops of string to make first a hand drum, then a Japanese harp and finally a river.

い

i

igloo

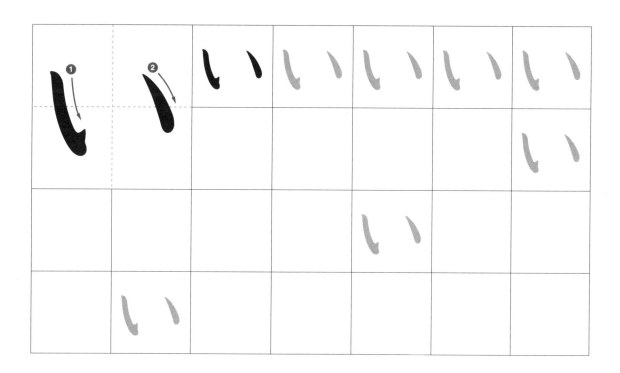

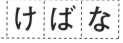

い　え

Remember to take your shoes off before you step inside an いえ or Japanese house. Traditionally, いえ were made of paper and wood. But now, most Japanese live in concrete apartment buildings that usually have at least one traditional room with sliding paper doors and woven straw たたみ mats on the floor.

い　け　ば　な

Originally an art for Japanese priests and samurai, いけばな, Japanese flower arrangement, is now practised by all kinds of women and men throughout the world. いけばな tries to recreate a miniature version of nature's spontaneous beauty and vitality. Try いけばな yourself and decorate your room or home with an original arrangement.

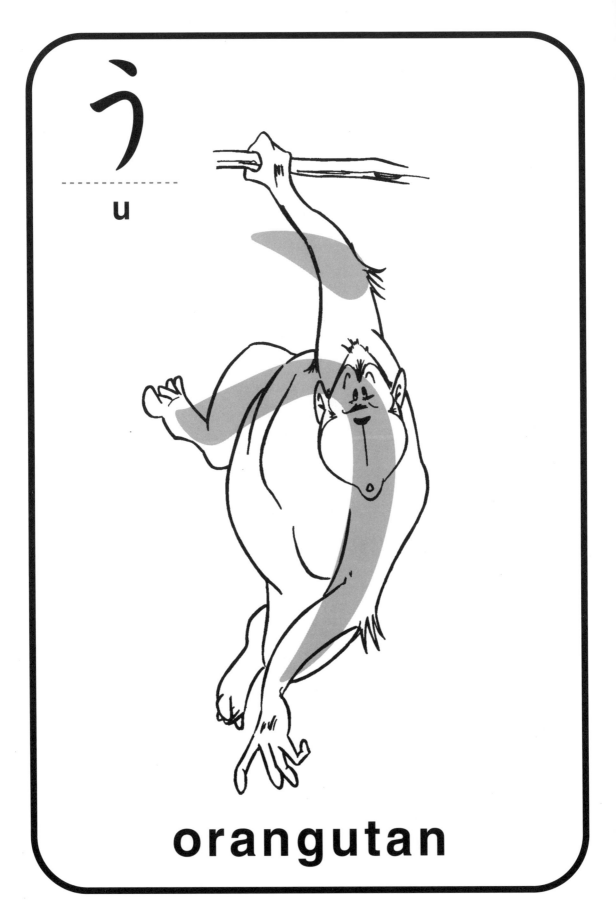

う

----

u

orangutan

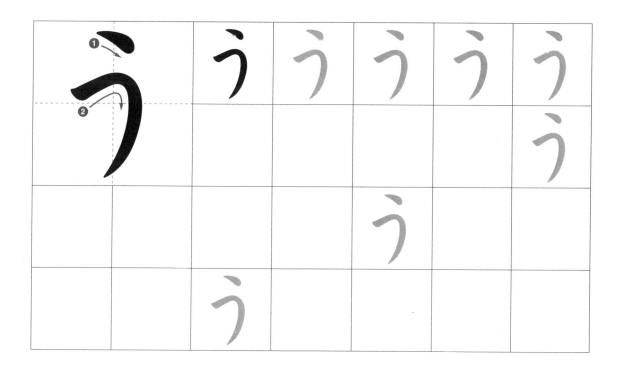

れんしゅう

| | ら | し | ま | た | ろ | う |

Young うらしまたろう rescues a turtle from a group of mean children. The turtle changes into a beautiful Sea Princess, who takes うらしまたろう to the Sea God's castle at the bottom of the ocean. After 3 happy years, うらしまたろう becomes homesick. Finally returning home, he finds himself a stranger. Unsure of what to do, うらしまたろう opens a box that the Sea Princess has given him but has forbidden him to open. Suddenly he becomes an old, old man; 3 years under the sea are equal to 300 years on land.

| | め | ぼ | し |

うめぼし might make you scrunch your face but they are known for healing upset stomachs and fighting exhaustion. Often eaten with rice, you may find an うめぼし or pickled plum, hidden in the middle of a rice ball.

17

え

e

elephant

れんしゅう

き べ ん

ん

"Get your boxed lunch. Get your boxed lunch." At every station on any long train ride in Japan, vendors call out from stands or walk up and down the aisles, selling えきべん, station boxed lunches. All えきべん contain rice with portions of other dishes like teriyaki chicken or fish and vegetables. Buying an えきべん with the local specialty from where you started or where you are going adds to the adventure of a train journey.

えん is Japanese money. There are six coins, worth 1, 5, 10, 50, 100 and 500 yen and three bills, worth 1,000, 5,000 and 10,000 yen. If you meet someone you like you can give them a five yen coin and say, 「ごえんがある」which means both "We have something in common" and "Here's a five yen coin."

お

o

ostrich

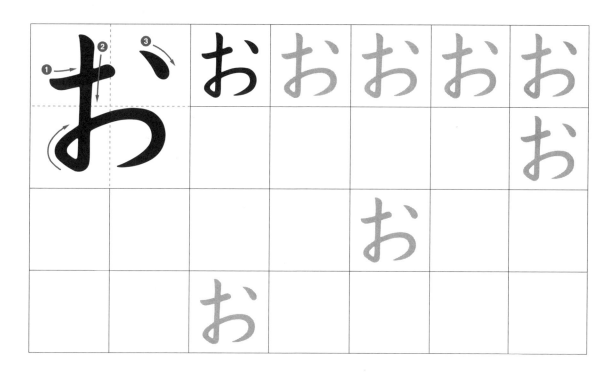

 りがみ

 に

Golden grasshoppers, magenta morning glories, green guppies and blue butterflies—with some colourful square sheets of papers, おりがみ, the Japanese art of paper-folding, allows you to create a fantastic world. Or, if you fold a thousand cranes, according to popular Japanese belief, you can live a thousand years! Give it a try with some friends, following the pictures below.

Play おにごっこ—the Japanese game of tag—the rules are just the same. Instead of "it," the おに is the person who chases. The おに appears as the villain in this game and in many Japanese folktales and legends, such as ももたろう. Sometimes, the おに has a kinder side, like when it leads a parade, majestically sweeping away all the evil influences that lay before its path.

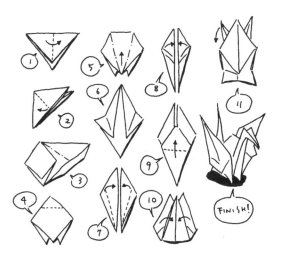

ka

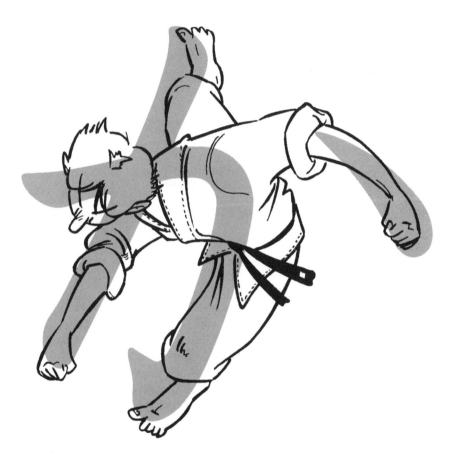

karate

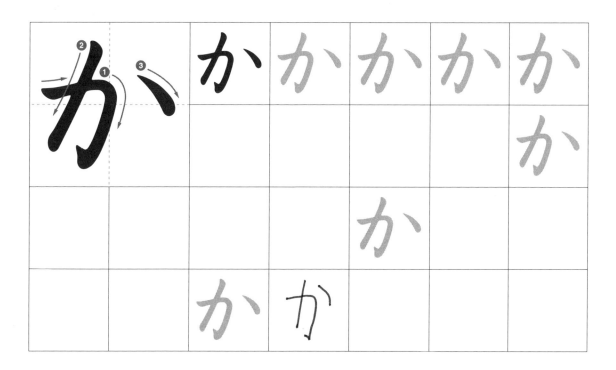

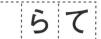 ら て

 ぶ き

からて means "empty hand". It was developed on the island of Okinawa as a means of self-defence. The Tokugawa Shogunate at the time forbid the use of weapons by anybody but the samurai. Now からて is a popular sport enjoyed by people of all ages around the world. Do you know someone with a black belt in からて?

Draw back the black, green and orange-striped curtains and the extravaganza of かぶき theatre begins. With dance, music and acrobatics, eye-catching costumes and exaggerated make-up, かぶき actors dazzle the audience, enacting dramas of love, treachery and loyalty. Using face paint, follow the contours of your face muscles to look like a かぶき character.

き
ki

kimono

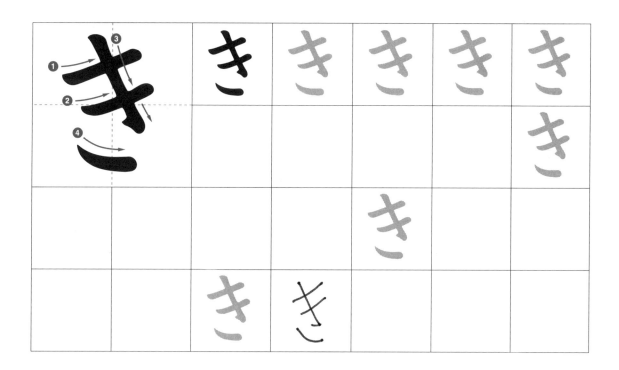

 もの

きもの, traditional Japanese dress for both men and women, are rectangular-sleeved, ankle length, silk robes tied around the hip by a thick sash called an おび. While very few people continue to wear きもの on a daily basis, special ceremonies and rituals still call for きもの, each event requiring a different style to reflect the occasion, season and time of day.

 つね

As the messengers of the deity of grain, sculptures of foxes, often stand on the grounds of Japanese shrines. But きつね, foxes, have another side to them. Charming and clever animals, きつね are often depicted as bewitching people and possessing special powers. In many Japanese folktales, a fox takes on human form in order to deceive people.

ku

cook

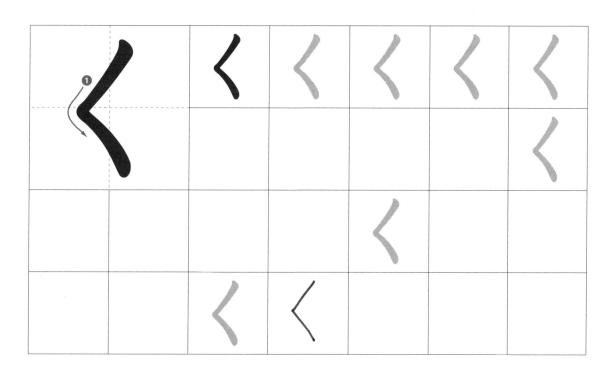

Pull the five coloured strings dangling from a く す だ ま and scented confetti showers all those standing below. Hung from ceilings, くすだま are balls ornamented with paper flowers and brocade cloth. Used for celebrations like the opening of a store, winning of a contest, or end of a sucessful play, くすだま were originally used on Boy's Day to ward off malice and dirtiness, hence its name くす だま, or balls of medicine.

3x3=9, 3x4=12, 3x5=15... Like all kids in elementary school, Japanese students must memorize their multiplication tables. Nine nines, or くく, is the name of a Japanese multiplication table that starts from 1x1 and ends with 9x9. How far can you go, multiplying in Japanese?

け

ke

kendo

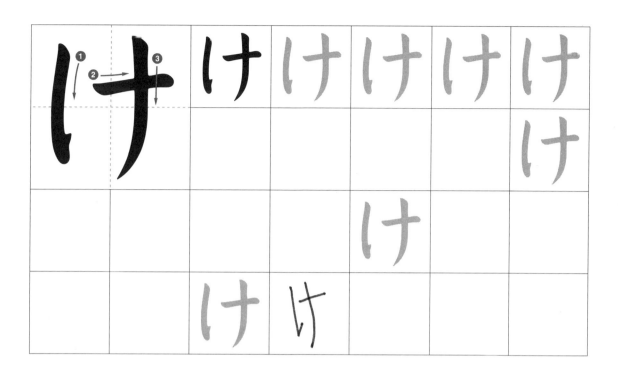

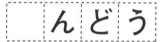
れんしゅう

□ んどう

Popular as a school sport and practised by police in Japan, けんどう disciplines the body and spirit. Originally based on samurai sword-fighting, けんどう has developed into a martial art that uses bamboo sticks and is now enjoyed by men and women in many countries outside Japan.

□ んだま

A popular wooden toy, けんだま is a game that has amused Japanese children for over 50 years. The object of the game is very simple—catch the ball in one of the cups. But there also many other けんだま tricks requiring different levels of skill to interest even today's children.

こ

ko

computer

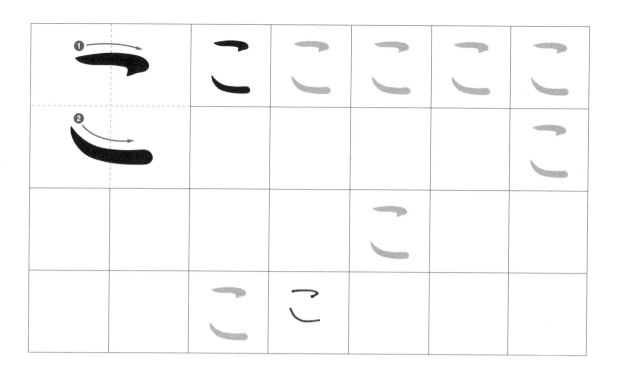

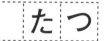

れんしゅう

	い	の	ぼ	り

	た	つ

Every May 5th, Children's Day, families decorate the roofs and windows of their homes with black, red and blue こいのぼり carp streamers. Families hang こいのぼり to express hope for their son's success and health. When the spring winds blow, the fins of the こいのぼり move and the carp swims in the air, like the carp in the old Chinese legend who swam upstream to become a fierce and powerful dragon.

On cold winter days, people in Japan warm themselves by sitting beneath a こたつ, a low-standing heated table. A こたつ has an electric heater underneath the table frame. A thick blanket, thrown over the table frame, falls to the feet of the こたつ, entrapping the hot air from the heater. A tabletop is fitted above the blanket, so that people can read, write and eat, while keeping their feet and lower bodies warm beneath the こたつ.

さ

sa

samurai

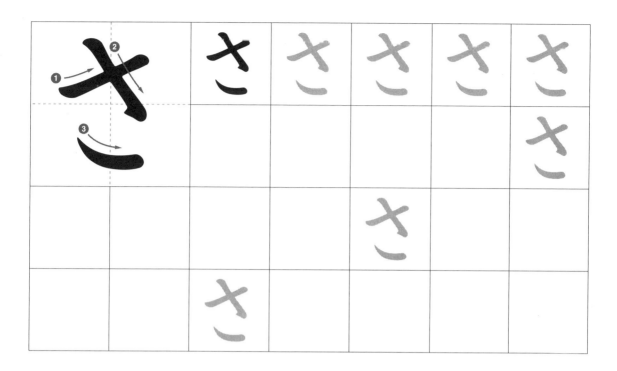

れんしゅう

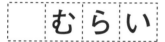 むらい

 くら

Japan's knights, さむらい followed the ぶしどう code, which gave their lords full control over their own lives. さむらい were trained in six martial arts—judo, archery, horseback riding, fencing, spearmanship and firearm—and were always at the beck and call of their lords to provide an army and wage battles.

Japanese visit parks and public gardens every spring to see the さくら, cherry blossoms. People picnic and party beneath the pink and white blossoms of さくら, marvelling at the beauty of nature when a slight wind sends showers of petals into the air.

し

shi

sheep

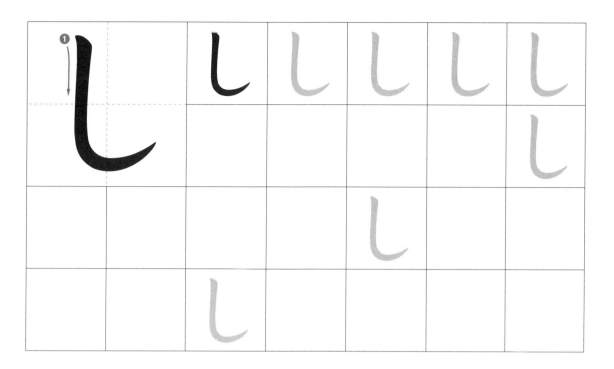

し | ろ

A labyrinth of moats, walls, watch towers and false pathways of the しろ or castle protected the lord and his retainers from their enemies. Most しろ were built in the seventeenth to nineteenth century, as fortresses and economic and administrative centres of feudal lords. Though few original しろ remain, one stands in Himeiji called the White Heron for its beautiful white walls seem to soar to the sky.

し | ち | ご | さ | ん

Three- and seven-year old girls in bright kimonos and five-year old boys in miniature suits crowd shrines on しちごさん, the 7-5-3 Festival. しちごさん, held on November 15th, is when parents pray for their children's safe and healthy future. After the visit they buy their sons and daughters ちとせあめ ("thousand year candy"), with sweet wishes that their children may live so long.

35

す

su

sumo

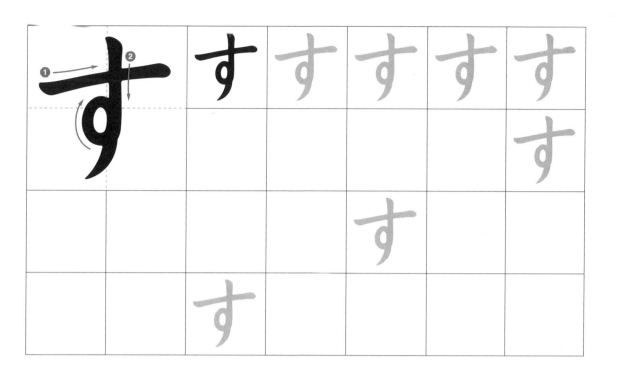

□ し

□ も う

Thin slices of raw fish on top of riceballs, すし is a Japanese delicacy. Sold in Japan at restaurants, supermarkets and take-out shops and made at home, すし tastes best when dipped in soy sauce with a little わさび or horseradish.

After stamping their feet and throwing salt in the air, すもう wrestlers push, throw, trip, shove and lift their opponents out of the ring or onto the ring's floor. The wrestlers of this 2000 year old sport are enormous, weighing an average 326 pounds or 148 kilogrammes. They wear loincloths and have ちょんまげ, long hair greased back and tied up in a knot. Try playing Japan's national sport with your friends, using a rope to make a ring.

せ

se

centipede

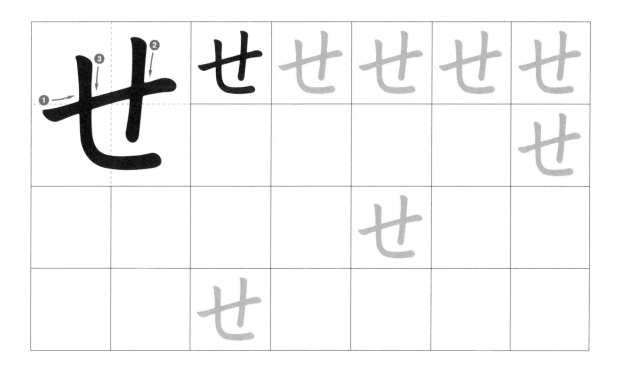

つ ぶ ん

ん と う

Ghosts in closets and behind shower curtains; demons beneath beds and in cupboards, flee their hiding places and run out the homes of Japanese every February 3rd on せつぶん. せつぶん is the day Japanese rid their homes of all the ghosts and demons lurking about by yelling,「おにはそと，ふくはうち」or "Out with the demons! In with good luck!" and throwing beans inside and outside the house. After completing the job, everyone eats as many beans as they are years old.

With large baths the size of pools—some with herbal medicines, other with spas—せんとう, or public baths, are a place to wash, relax and gossip with neighbours. Go to a せんとう and you will see little girls bathing with their mothers in the women's section while young boys scrub their father's backs in the men's section. Whether at home or a せんとう, the Japanese wash and rinse themselves outside before soaking in the tubs.

そ

so

sorcerer

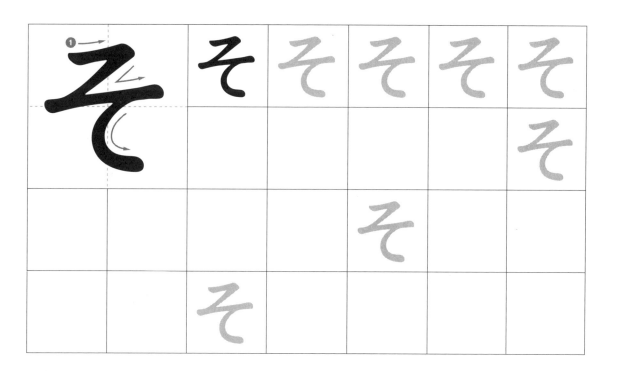

れんしゅう

□ば

□ろ□ば□ん

When you move to a new place in Japan, you often give your new neighbours そば. そば is Japanese buckwheat noodles but そば can also mean "next to". So, by giving your new neighbours そば, you are greeting them and saying that you've moved next door. And on New Year's Eve, Japanese often eat としこしそば, or "crossing-over-into-the-New-Year-noodles," so that your fortune may extend into the New Year, like the long noodles of the そば.

A そろばん is a Japanese abacus. All children receive そろばん instruction in elementary school. Many shopkeepers can do sums quicker with a そろばん than with a pocket calculator. So while そろばん may seem old-fashioned, it is still preferred by some Japanese.

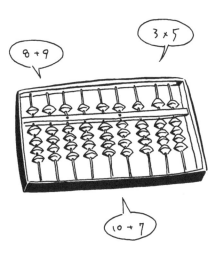

た

ta

target

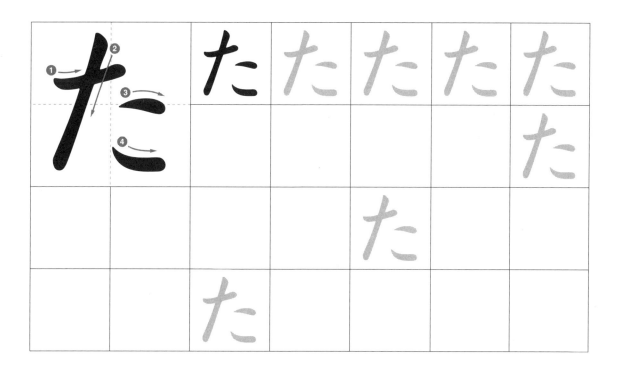

れんしゅう

□こ

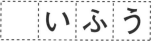
□いふう

Riding the winds, warriors and dragons on large kites fly and fight in the air, trying to bring each other down in the annual kite wars. Around 50 people are required to manoeuver one of these huge kites. Japanese kites, or たこ, are spectacular crafts made from bamboo and paper. Once thought to link heaven and earth, children and adults fly たこ on New Year's Day and as soon as strong winds blow.

Whirling from the ocean, たいふう, or typhoons, tear through Japan and other islands in the Pacific Ocean. たいふう are like hurricanes, whirlwind storms that are about 300 miles or 500 kilometres wide with a calm centre area called the eye. Typhoons cause much damage from August through October but their strong winds have twice stopped the Mongols from invading Japan.

ち

chi

chimpanzee

ち ち ち ち ち ち ち ち ち ち

| | ん | ど | ん | や |

| | | か | て | つ |

「ちんちんちん」 rings the gongs. 「どんどんどん」 bellows the drums. ちんどんや are street performers who announce the opening of a play, event, store, or building. With their flamboyant face paint, wigs and costumes, ちんどんや walk up and down the streets, playing their instruments, passing out flyers and catching the attention of potential customers walking by.

With twelve ちかてつ, or subway lines and numerous other street level trains that connect to the subway, Tokyo's subway maps look like a maze of colours. Yet everyday, over eight million people weave their way in and out of different subway lines, to get to and from work, school, or play. Over 300 miles or 500 kilometres of subway tracks beneath Japanese cities help people move about.

45

つ

tsu

tsunami

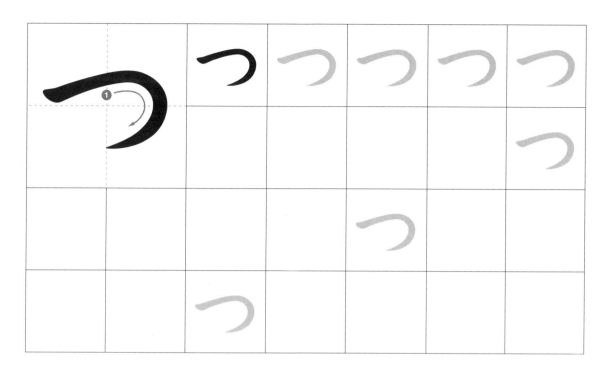

 な み

つなみ are awesome tidal waves caused by earth-quakes and volcanoes rumbling under the sea. つなみ can rise as high as 100 feet or 30 metres and cause massive damage and fatalities in coastal cities. つなみ is now used in English to describe such waves.

 ゆ

The rainy season lasts for one month from mid-June to mid-July in Japan. It is wet, moldy, grey and very humid during the つゆ, with 30-40% of the annual rainfall falling at this time. This sounds unpleasant, but without つゆ Japan's rice crop would be destroyed by the intense heat of summer.

47

て

te

telephone

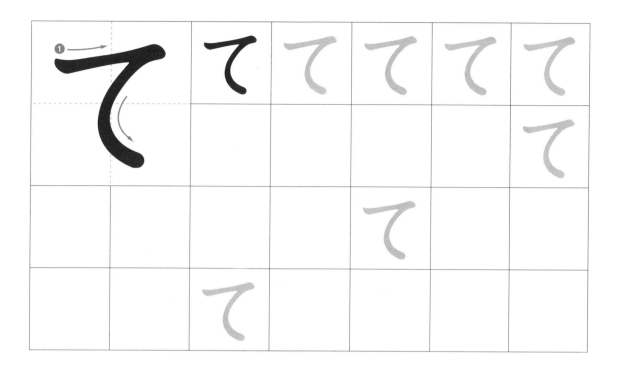

☐ んぐ

With golden, gleaming eyes and teeth, てんぐ have been known to abduct children and priests deep into the mountains. Part man, part bird, てんぐ have the body and limbs of human beings, wings and a long nose protruding from their red faces. Yet in moments of kindness, this mountain guardian acts as a protector, using its supernatural powers to help humankind.

☐ るてるぼうず

In dreary weather, Japanese kids hang a てるてるぼうず by a window or door. A simple, small ghost-like doll, a てるてるぼうず is a charm for good weather. Make your own and see if it works. Push the stuffing up to make a round head and secure at the neck with string. If good weather comes, thank your てるてるぼうず by drawing a face on its head. If you want rain, not sunshine, colour your てるてるぼうず head black before hanging it up.

と

to

toboggan

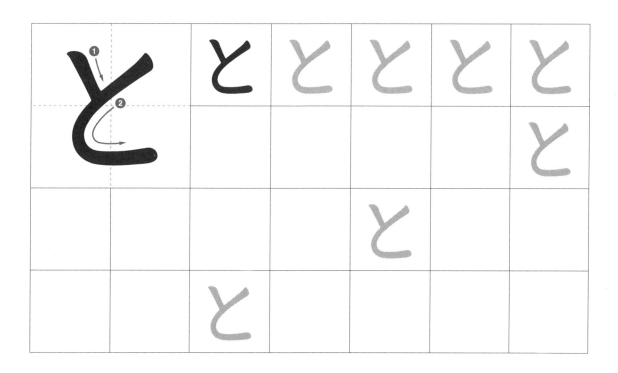

| | う | き | ょ | う |

| | う | ふ |

Around twelve million people live in とうきょう, Japan's capital located by the Pacific Ocean on Japan's main island. When とうきょう was called Edo and the shogun lived in the present imperial palace, とうきょう was the largest city in the world. Now とうきょう is the seventh largest city in the world.

Made from soybeans and packed with protein, とうふ, is something parents love to serve their kids. とうふ is eaten in many ways—とうふ steak, fried とうふ, とうふ dip, とうふ with vegetables, stir-fried とうふ with beef. Try putting some fresh とうふ into a salad or use some in your next lasagna dish, instead of ricotta cheese and see if you like it.

な

na

Napoleon

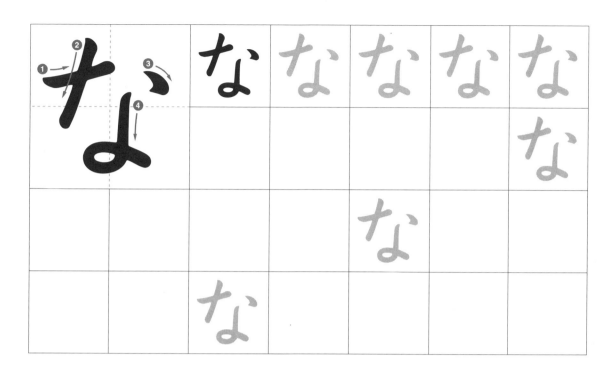

れんしゅう

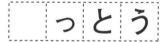

っとう

Sticky, smelly, fermented soybeans, なっとう is commonly mixed with a raw egg, soy sauce and some mustard and eaten over hot rice. If you go to Japan, will you give it a try? Japanese often tell how used to Japan you've become by seeing if you can eat a なっとう concoction.

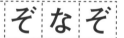

ぞなぞ

What has only one eye and one leg? A needle! What can't you hold with your right hand? Your right hand!! なぞなぞ are simple, silly "What is it?" jokes. Entertainers called riddle priests once stood on the streets of Japan, challenging those passing by with なぞなぞ. Though you won't find riddle priests anymore, chances are there is at least one なぞなぞ teller in your class.

ni

ninja

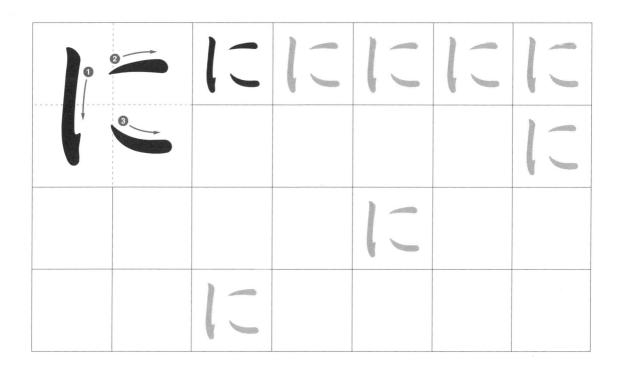

れんしゅう

□ ん じゃ

んじゃ could sneak into enemy territories, attack enemy leaders, leaving their missions accomplished as the only trace that they had been there. にんじゃ, master Japanese spies, worked for warring lords during Japan's civil wars. Their secrets skills, envied by others, were passed down by word of mouth from one にんじゃ to another.

□ ん て ん ど う

With the control panel in your hand, you decide the fate of sailors defending their ship from pirates, sumo wrestlers fighting street gangs, and an empress trekking through jungles in search of hidden treasures.This is the world of にんてんどう video games. Parents may hate it, but にんてんどう has spread from Japan to every corner of the world.

nu

noodles

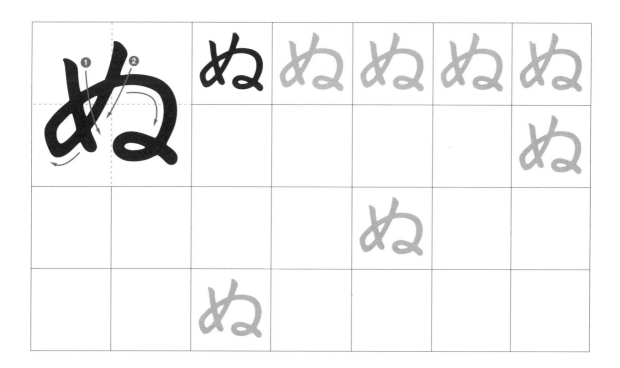

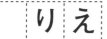

りえ

"Fill in the pictures by colouring inside the lines," the directions say in a Japanese colouring book, ぬりえ, like colouring books everywhere. Small children colour their ぬりえ, making castles むらさき, purple, giraffes look like tigers with stripes of きいろ, yellow, and くろ, black, and pianos みどり, green.

いぐるみ

ぬいぐるみ are stuffed animals. Go to a game arcade in Japan and you have a chance of winning a ぬいぐるみ for 100 yen with a game of UFO Catcher. In this game, you position a pair of robotic hands above one of the ぬいぐるみ that fills the gamebox. Push the button that lowers the hands and with some luck, they will grab you a ぬいぐるみ.

ne

net

 つけ

Merchants hugging bags of money, monkeys drinking rice wine, a famous warrior riding a horse and other heroes, animals and humorous characters are the objects of ねつけ, miniature ivory carvings. Until the nineteenth century, Japanese people used ねつけ to keep the ends of cords or sashes on their clothing in place. But with the change to Western dress, ねつけ are now collector's items enjoyed for their detailed work and humour.

んがじょう

To wish relatives, friends and business associates a prosperous and healthy New Year, Japanese send out ねんがじょう, special New Year's post-cards. ねんがじょう have a special symbol below their stamps. When the people at the post office see this symbol, they know to hold the card until the first of January when all the cards are delivered at once. For a few extra yen, a government-issued ねんがじょう gives the recipient a shot at winning a prize. At the bottom of these ねんがじょう are a sequence of numbers. Every year, on live television, an archer strikes a rotating target to pick the numbers for the winning combination.

の

no

knot

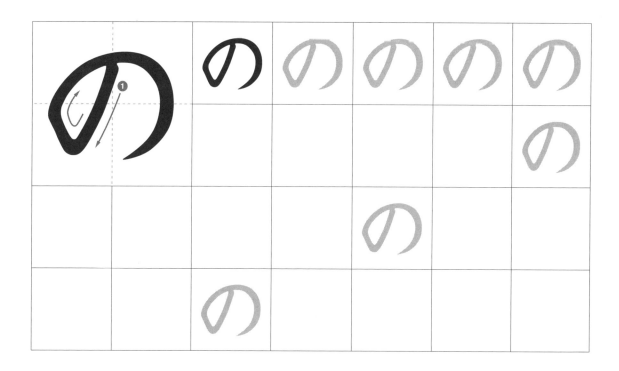

れんしゅう

れ　ん

う

Originally hung in front of doors and windows, のれん, thick, cloth split curtains kept heat and dust out of homes and stores. Later shopkeepers started to print のれん with a boldly designed emblem to advertise the name of their shop. Now のれん are used by stores and restaurants to indicate they are open, and in homes as room dividers and decoration.

Gods, demons and ghosts of warriors and lovers appear in のう, telling their stories of duels, and nature's beauty in elegant poetic language. のう is traditional Japanese drama performed by actors who wear elaborate costumes and eerie life-like masks. Slow and deliberate at the beginning, のう often ends with frenzied dance and music.

は

ha

harmonica

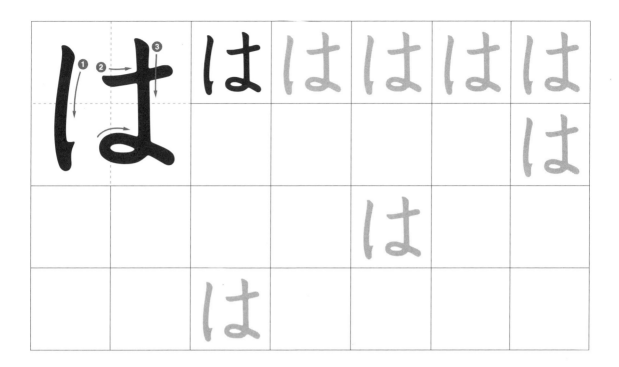

な ふ だ

Pines in January, plums in February and cherry blossom in March—for every month of the year, a suit of four cards patterned with that month's flower or tree and a poem or animal make up a pack of cards in はなふだ, the flower card game. The basic object of はなふだ is to get as many points as possible by matching up the suits of four cards.

ん こ

Where we sign our name, Japanese stamp their はんこ or seals. はんこ stamps an impression of a person's name, showing that they endorse a document, agreement or transaction. Made of plastic, wood or ivory, each はんこ, like a fingerprint is supposedly different from any other.

ひ

hi

hippo

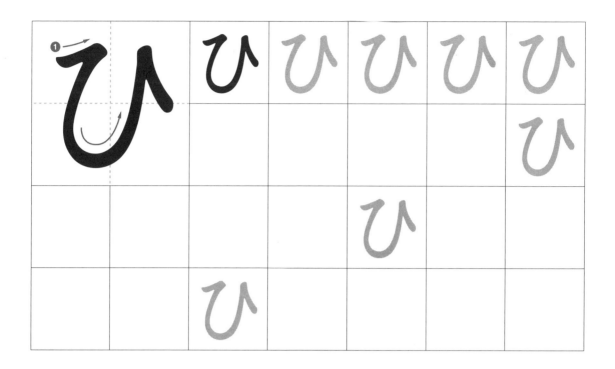

□な│ま│つ│り

Rows of dolls dressed in the costumes of the Japanese court nobles of long ago decorate the homes of those celebrating the ひなまつり Doll Festival. ひなまつり is held every March 3rd. While the drummer dolls strike their drums, dolls of ox pull carriages and the dolls of the Emperor and Empress look on from the top row, young girls in colourful kimonos feast with their families on diamond-shaped rice cakes.

□き│ゃ│く

With swords on their backs to fight highway bandits, ひきゃく, couriers, could run 300 miles or 500 kilometres in four days. ひきゃく once ran between cities delivering messages and small packages for warlords and merchants. Modern day courier services have replaced ひきゃく with trains, planes, cars and bicycles.

ふ

----

fu

hula hoop

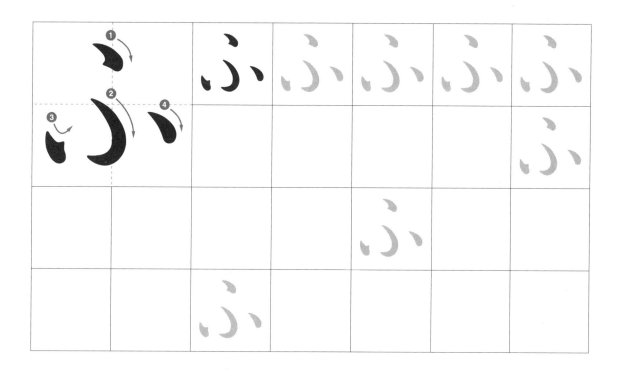

れ・ん・し・ゅ・う

と ん

く わ ら い

While more and more Japanese sleep in beds, most still choose to sleep on ふとん. ふとん are thick quilted matresses. Japanese fold their ふとん and put it in the closet in the morning and lay it out on the floor to go to sleep at night. Using a ふとん conserves space—a room for sleeping at night can become a living room by day.

Japan's version of "Pin the Tail on the Donkey," ふくわらい, traditionally played during the New Year holidays, is easy to make and play. On a large sheet of paper, draw an outline of a person's face. Then cut out eyes, eyebrows, a nose and a mouth for the face on a separate sheet of paper. Take turns being blindfolded with your friends and see whose's best at putting the features in place. Try not to laugh during other people's turns or they'll know that they've made a mistake. But then again, half the fun is seeing the strange faces made by playing ふくわらい.

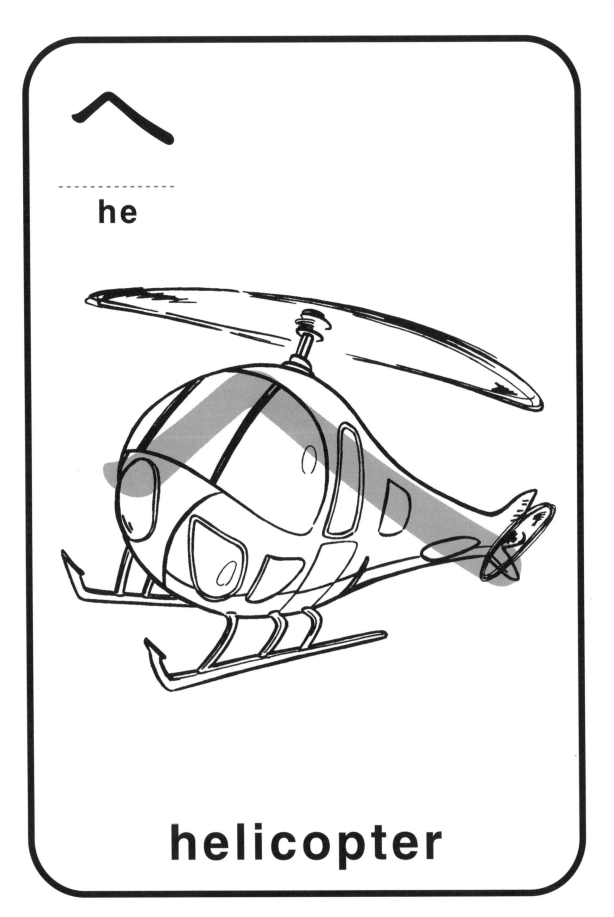

he

helicopter

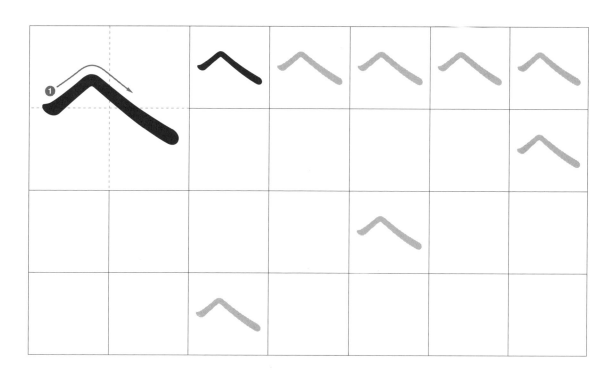

By writing out this combination of hiragana letters, you can draw a face of a quizzical person. The first two へ are the eyebrows, the の are the eyes, the も is a nose and the last へ is the mouth. じ is a し that makes up the outline of the face with two dashes placed to the top right of the face. Do you know anyone with a へのへのもへじ face?

Great battles, powerful leaders, tragic romances and a sense that all glory must come to an end fill へいけものがたり, Japan's epic novel. へいけものがたり recounts the rise and fall of a clan in medieval Japan. Once told by professional storytellers who wandered about Japan, awing their audiences with their dramatic retellings, へいけものがたり remains a popular story, read at school and re-enacted in plays.

ほ
ho

hovercraft

し

Lovers torn apart by the Milky Way, the star Vega, the weaver for the Gods and the star Altair, the cowboy, only meet once a year. The meeting of these two ほし, or stars, is celebrated by the Japanese every year at the Tanabata Festival on July 7th. Celebrators write their wishes and romantic desires on colourful papers, hang them on bamboo stalks and place the stalks outside in hope that some of the lover's luck may fall upon them from the skies.

たる

Japanese are fascinated by insects like the firefly or ほたる. Children learn the story of the scholar, who too poor to buy a lamp, used to study by the light of ほたる. Nobles of another time held parties on summer nights so guests could watch the flickering lights of the ほたる.

ま

ma

mask

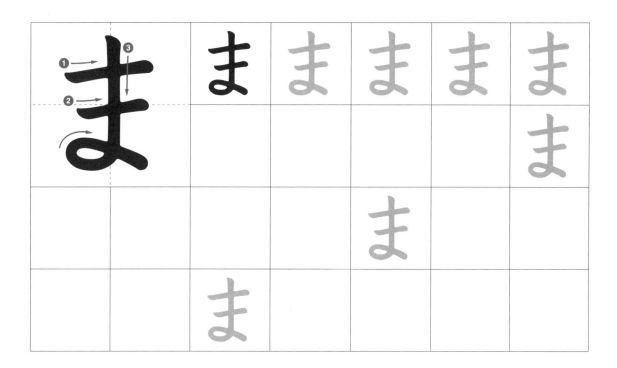

□んが

まんが, cartoons and comics, are a culture in Japan—there are まんが about everything for everybody. Boys read まんが about robots and racers, college students read まんが love stories, and business people learn how to use a computer from まんが while high school students use まんが to pass history exams.

□ねきねこ

With one paw raised, まねきねこ sit at the front of restaurants and stores and invite people in. Shopkeepers and business people regard these white pottery cats with a small bell around their necks as bearers of good fortune. Place your money in a まねきねこ coin bank and your fortunes may double!

み

----

mi

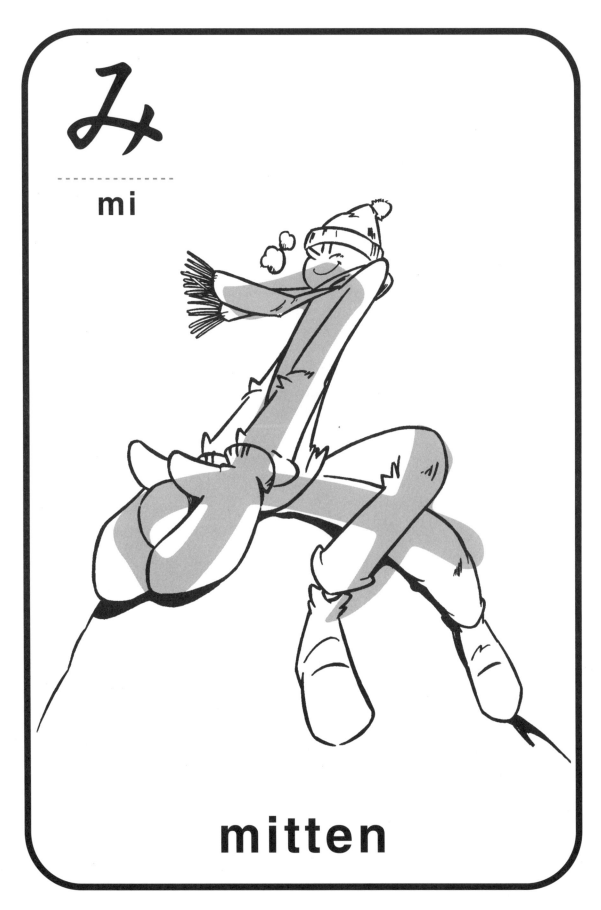

mitten

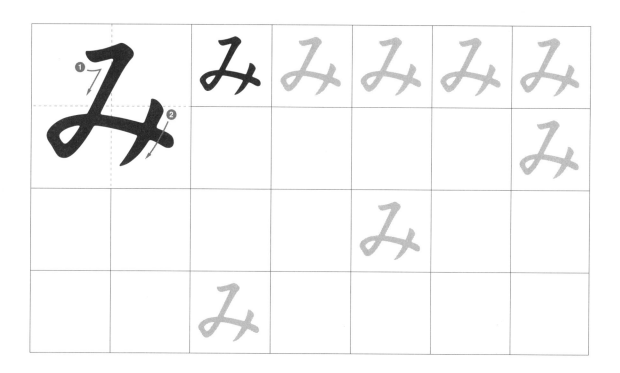

 こ し

 や げ

Every year, people carry their local god in a みこ
し, portable shrine, through their neighbourhood
streets. When the god forces the みこし to sway
left and right in a display of its power, the mov-
ers shout and heave the みこし, while crowds yell
from the sides. This festivity insures everyone of
the god's protection for another year.

Whenever a Japanese person takes a trip, they always return with みやげ, souvenir foods, crafts or
trinkets. みやげ let others enjoy the taste of an excursion and are also a form of thanks to family
and co-workers who took over the responsibilities
of the person who took time off to take a trip.

む

mu

moose

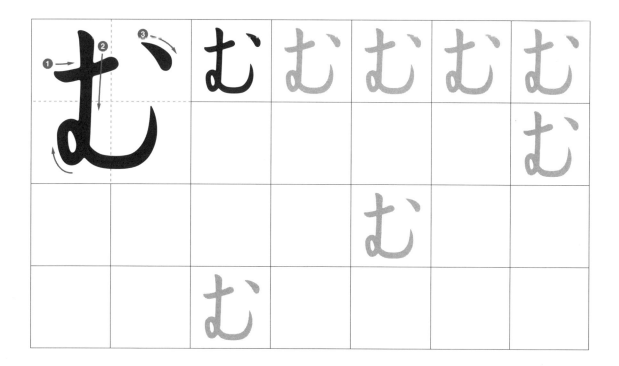

□し

Go to any Japanese toy store and you will find nets, magnifying glasses and cages of all shapes and sizes for むし, insects. One of Japanese kids' favourite hobbies is collecting むし: dragonflies, grasshoppers, cicadas, beetles, butterflies...

□かしばなし

People once used to go to storytellers to hear むかしばなし, folktales. Storytellers only told むかしばなし like ももたろう or うらしまたろう at night for mice were said to urinate from above if むかしばなし were told during the day. むかしばなし remain popular today, and are retold in books and on television.

むかし
むかし.....

め

me

merry-go-round

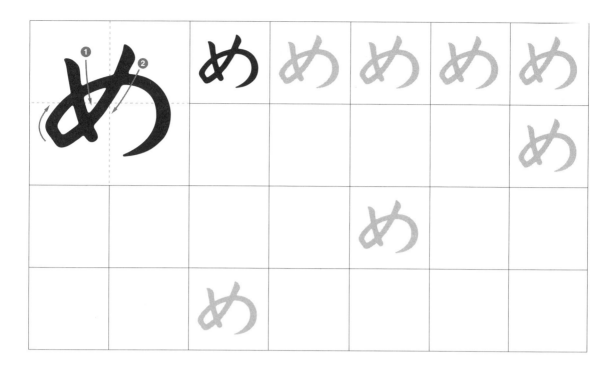

れんしゅう

□ い し

When meeting someone for the first time, Japanese exchange めいし namecards. People who work use company めいし with their name, position, and the company's name, address, and telephone number printed on the card. People also make personal めいし with their home address and telephone number. Write your name in ひらがな on a small piece of paper or card and exchange めいし with your classmates and friends.

□ ん こ

Since the twelfth century, Japanese children have been playing めんこ, a game that uses small square or round pieces decorated with the picture of a popular character or hero on one side. To play with your friends, make a めんこ piece by cutting out a circle or square from thick card and colour one side. Then place your めんこ on the ground and see if your opponent can flip it over by throwing his or her めんこ at your piece.

も

mo

monster

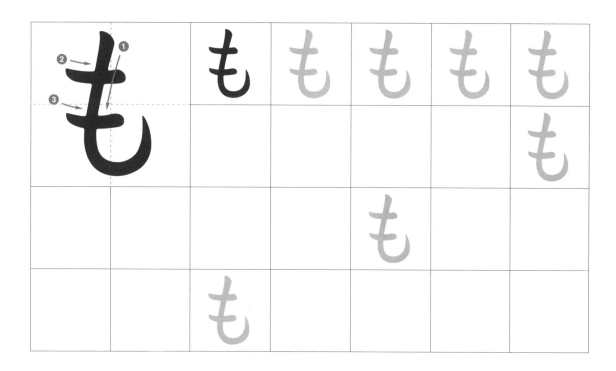

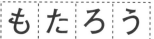

もち

Sticky, chewy and hard to swallow, もち is made by pounding boiled white rice. Once eaten only for celebrations like weddings and New Year's Day, もち is now sold all year round. もち can be eaten in hundreds of ways—toasted and dipped in soy sauce, put in fish soup, rolled in sweet powder or stuffed with sweet red beans. ももたろう's rice dumplings are made of もち.

ももたろう

Born from a peach found by an old woman doing her laundry on a riverbank, young ももたろう, the peach boy, grows into a healthy and strong young man. After ogres wreak havoc in his village, he sets off to conquer Ogre Island. With the elderly woman's rice dumplings and the help of a dog, monkey and pheasant whom he meets along the way, ももたろう fights the ogres until they promise not to cause any more trouble and returns home with treasures for all.

や

ya

yard

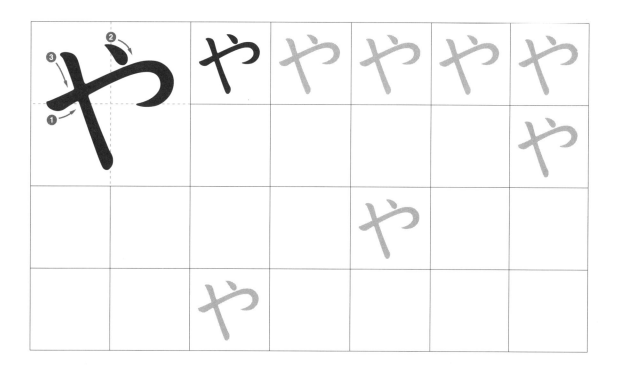

れんしゅう

	き	と	り

やきとり are small bite-size pieces of chicken, liver or chicken meatballs on bamboo skewers, basted in sauce and grilled over an open fire. People in Japan often relax with friends by drinking and eating やきとり at home, restaurants and street stalls.

	た	い

In the evenings to the early hours of morning, やたい are set up by train stations and off main streets. やたい are street stalls where locals and passerbys stop for a bowl of noodles, やきとり or simmered foods, and a glass of beer or rice wine. During festivals and temple fairs, lemonade, stir-fried noodles, sweets and games are sold from やたい.

ゆ

yu

unicorn

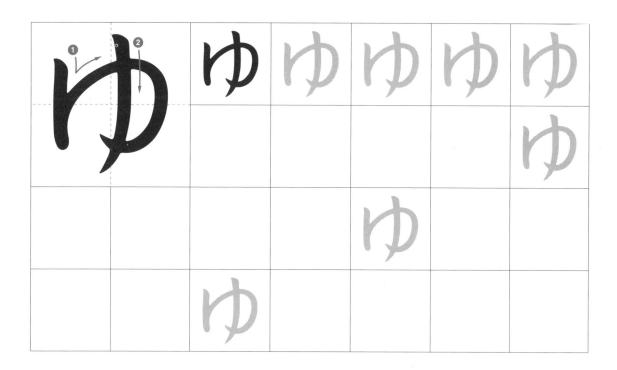

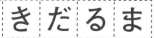

☐ か た

☐ き だ る ま

Once the common summer dress of the Japanese, now those staying at inns and hot spring resorts wear ゆかた before and after baths. Men, women and children enjoying summer festivals and shrine and temple fairs also dress in ゆかた. Children's ゆかた are often decorated with the motifs of popular cartoon characters.

When winter comes snow falls in all but the southern islands of Japan and children make ゆきだるま snowmen. Two balls of snow on top of each other, not three, forms a ゆきだるま. Every year in the northern city of Sapporo, five-storey high snow samurai tower over snow leopards and ゆきだるま at the Snow Festival.

yo

yacht

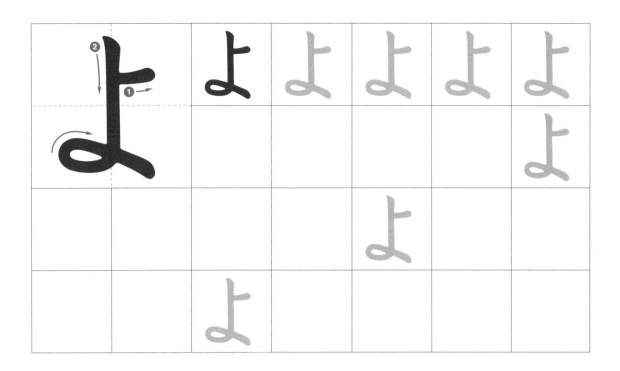

よろい

Wearing their よろい, archers ride proudly into battle. よろい are suits of armour first made in ninth century Japan. The segmented pieces of よろい, tied together by coloured strings and leather, allowed warriors free movement with maximum protection. Archers also wore rivet studded iron helmets that had long metal horns.

よびこう

よびこう are cram schools which help students to prepare for intensely competitive university entrance examinations. Though not an official part of the education system, some 200,000 よびこう are scattered throughout Japan. Students who have already failed the exams and high school students yet to sit them attend よびこう.

ら

ra

raccoon

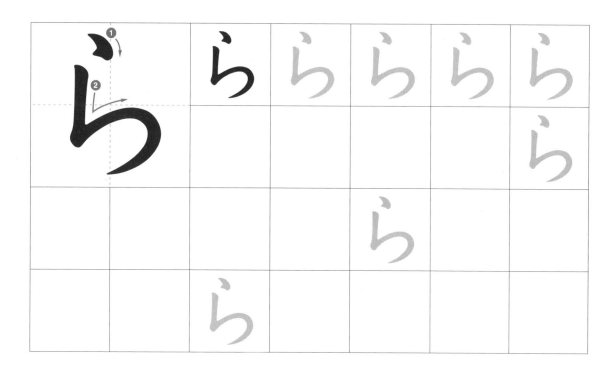

くご

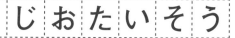

じおたいそう

Instantly changing from a young vain merchant to an old, tired mother, one らくご storyteller narrates an entire drama using only a folding fan and a hand towel as props to aid his or her facial and vocal expressions. らくご are humorous stories about human follies.

One, two, three, four, bend your knees, raise your arms. Five, six, seven, eight, stand up straight, lower your arms. Everyday, people all around Japan turn on their radios to practise らじおたいそう, radio exercises broadcasted three times a day. During the summer vacation, kids go to the local park to perform らじおたいそう with their grandparents and neighbours at 6:30 in the morning!

89

リ

ri

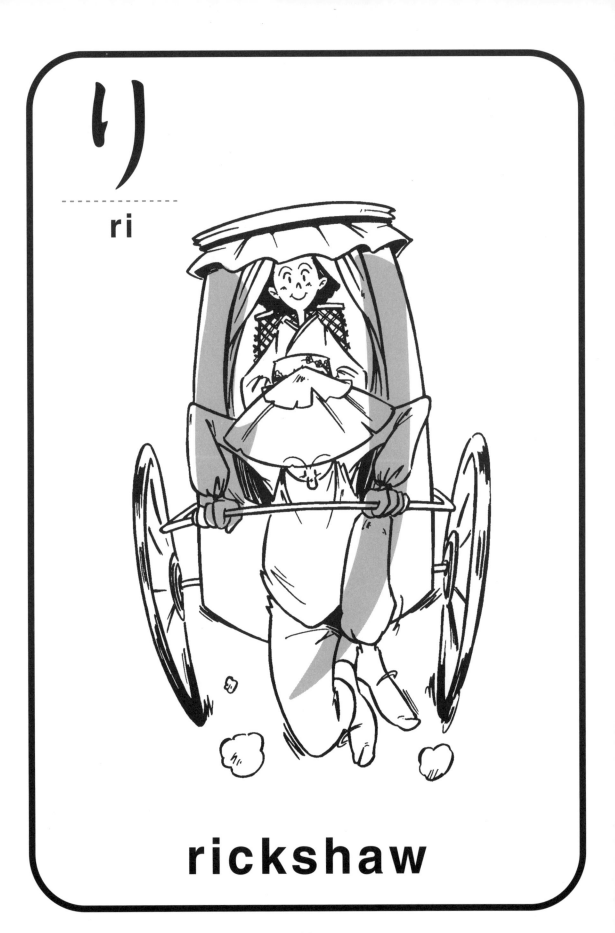

rickshaw

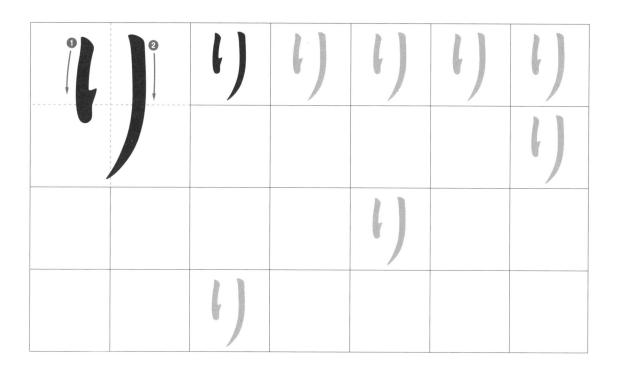

りゅう

Fabulous beasts, りゅう or dragons have a snake's body, scales, four legs with five talons on each foot, two horns, a long face, and a beard. When a りゅう rises from its home under the sea or beneath the earth's surface, rain, thunder and lightning fall from the sky.

りょかん

When Japanese want peace and quiet, they often retreat to a りょかん, Japanese inn. りょかん are found in the mountains, by the sea or in cities far from the crowded main streets with inner gardens. Guests are given ゆかた to wear before and after soaking in the りょかん's large indoor or open-air baths. They sleep in large traditional たたみ mat rooms.

る

ru

roo

	る	る	る	る	る
					る
			る		
	る				

れんしゅう

□ すばん

るすばん means staying behind and looking after the house when everybody else has gone is away. A るすばんでんわ or telephone answering machine will take messages when you're out at work, school and play.

93

re

reptile

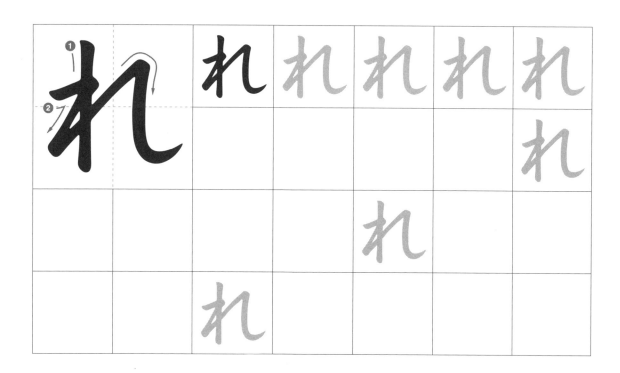

れんしゅう

 っしゃ

 んこん

Local trains, express trains excursion trains, freight trains, bullet trains, electric trains—the word れっしゃ includes every type of train. In a country where there are so many people living in such little space れっしゃ help people move around and keep roads from becoming too crowded. You can see every type of れっしゃ in Japan, from steam locomotives now used as tourist trains to the famous monorail.

Dipped in batter and deep-fried in oil as a tempura dish, or scattered on top of vinegared rice with fish, shrimp and eggs, れんこん are crunchy lotus roots eaten by Japanese in traditional foods. When cut like a carrot into flat circular pieces, れんこん resembles a bicycle wheel.

roller coaster

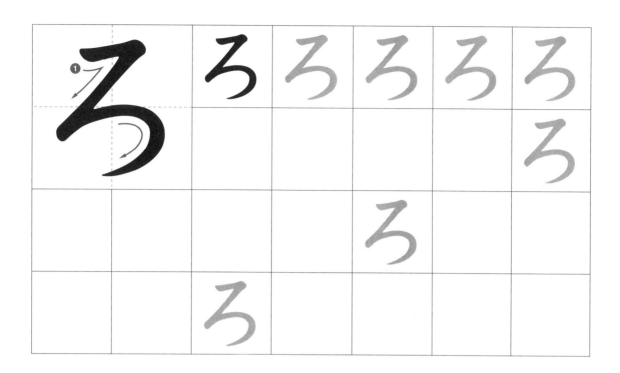

うにん

Samurai without lords to serve were the ろうにん, floating people, of seventeenth to nineteenth century Japan. High school graduates who cram to get into a university are modern day ろうにん. Some students may have to spend two or three years being ろうにん before they can pass the tough exams to get into the university of their choice.

くろ

Since ancient times, Japanese have been making pottery. ろくろ, potter's wheels have been used for over 2,000 years in Japan. Ceramic vessels were used to store precious grains of wheat and rice. Pottery remains a highly esteemed craft with different styles found in every region.

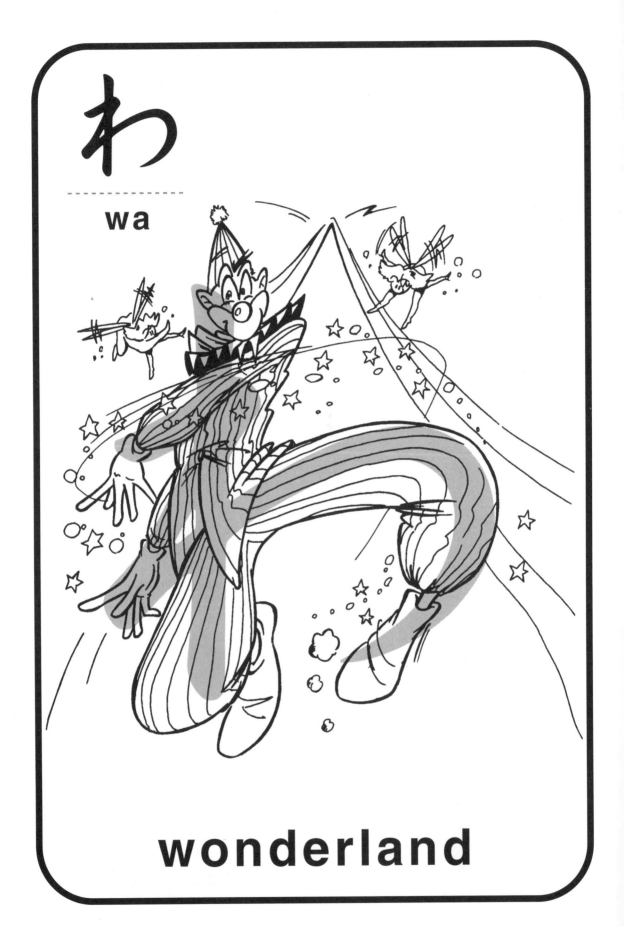

わ

wa

wonderland

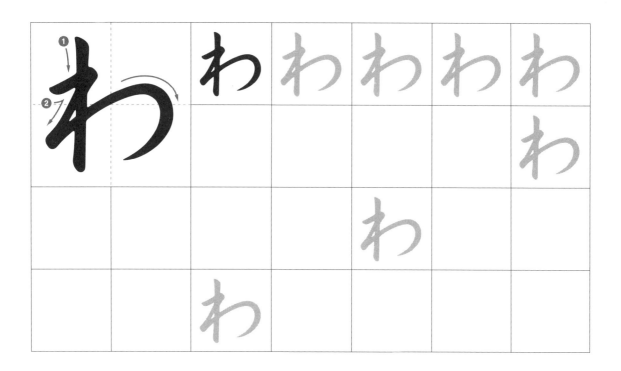

れんしゅう

□	た	し

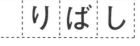

□	り	ば	し

わたし means "I" and can be used by anybody on any occasion. Practise using わたし with your friends. Introducing yourself:「わたしはたろうです」which means "I am Taro." Stating what you like:「わたしはすしがすきです」which means "I like sushi." Stating what you dislike:「わたしはくくがきらいです」which means "I don't like multiplication tables."

わりばし are disposable wooden chopsticks provided for guests and restaurant customers. They are wrapped in paper and must be split apart before use. Recently many restaurants have stopped using わりばし in favour of reusable plastic chopsticks. This helps to save forests all around the world.

を

(w)o

octopus

を を を を を を を を を

ひらがな
べんきょうする

にほんご
べんきょうする

を marks the result, goal or focus of a verb. For example in 「ひらがなをべんきょうする」 or "I study hiragana," the を after ひらがな tells you that it is "hiragana" that you are studying. Similarly, in 「にほんごをべんきょうする」 or "I study Japanese," the を after にほんご tells you that it is "Japanese" that you are studying.

101

ん

n

pen

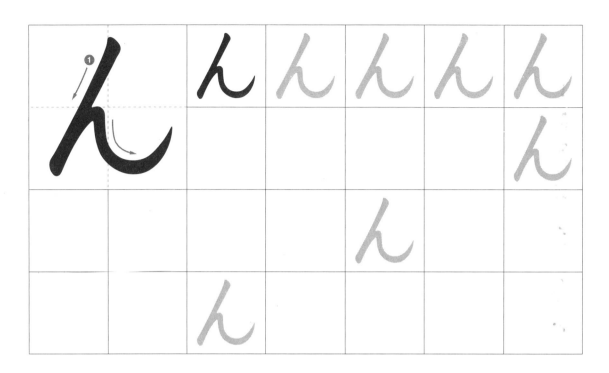

う

う と

While ん appears in the middle of words like け んどう and at the end of words like えん, no Japanese word begins with the hiragana ん. ん is commonly used in colloquial expressions such as 「う ん」 which means "yeah" or "okay" and 「うんと」 which is a sound people make when they lift a heavy weight.

FULL HIRAGANA CHART

1	あ a	い i	う u	え e	お o
2	か ka	き ki	く ku	け ke	こ ko
3	さ sa	し shi	す su	せ se	そ so
4	た ta	ち chi	つ tsu	て te	と to
5	な na	に ni	ぬ nu	ね ne	の no
6	は ha	ひ hi	ふ fu / hu	へ he	ほ ho
7	ま ma	み mi	む mu	め me	も mo
	や ya	(い) i	ゆ yu	(え) e	よ yo
	ら ra	り ri	る ru	れ re	ろ ro
	わ wa	(い)	(う)	(え)	を o
	ん n				

が ga	ぎ gi	ぐ gu	げ ge	ご go
ざ za	じ ji	ず zu	ぜ ze	ぞ zo
だ da	ぢ ji	づ zu	で de	ど do
ば ba	び bi	ぶ bu	べ be	ぼ bo
ぱ pa	ぴ pi	ぷ pu	ぺ pe	ぽ po

きゃ kya	きゅ kyu	きょ kyo
しゃ sha	しゅ shu	しょ sho
ちゃ cha	ちゅ chu	ちょ cho
にゃ nya	にゅ nyu	にょ nyo
ひゃ hya	ひゅ hyu	ひょ hyo
みゃ mya	みゅ myu	みょ myo
りゃ rya	りゅ ryu	りょ ryo
ぎゃ gya	ぎゅ gyu	ぎょ gyo
じゃ ja	じゅ ju	じょ jo
ぢゃ ja	ぢゅ ju	ぢょ jo
びゃ bya	びゅ byu	びょ byo
ぴゃ pya	ぴゅ pyu	ぴょ pyo

ひらがな
がんばって。

104

CONTRACTED HIRAGANA CHART

Here are some interesting combinations. These sounds are formed by adding a small や, ゆ or よ to the hiragana character.

きゃ kya	きゅ kyu	きょ kyo
しゃ sha	しゅ shu	しょ sho
ちゃ cha	ちゅ chu	ちょ cho
にゃ nya	にゅ nyu	にょ nyo
ひゃ hya	ひゅ hyu	ひょ hyo
みゃ mya	みゅ myu	みょ myo
りゃ rya	りゅ ryu	りょ ryo
ぎゃ gya	ぎゅ gyu	ぎょ gyo
じゃ ja	じゅ ju	じょ jo
ぢゃ ja	ぢゅ ju	ぢょ jo
びゃ bya	びゅ byu	びょ byo
ぴゃ pya	ぴゅ pyu	ぴょ pyo

れんしゅう

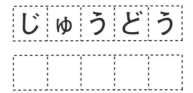

じゅうどう

じゅうどう was developed over 100 years ago when かのうじごろう established the こうどうかん どうじょう. じゅうどう means "the way of gentleness." It is a popular form of weaponless self-defence in Japan and other countries.

Throw the opponent from standing.

Hold the opponent down.

Hold the opponent's joints.

105

TWO-DASHES HIRAGANA CHART

The chart below shows the two-dash hiragana symbols. The Japanese put two dashes on the top right-hand corner of some hiragana so that they can represent more sounds. These dashes are called ちょんちょん, てんてん or だくてん and when added to the symbols the pronunciation changes.

が ga	ぎ gi	ぐ gu	げ ge	ご go
ざ za	じ ji	ず zu	ぜ ze	ぞ zo
だ da	ぢ ji	づ zu	で de	ど do
ば ba	び bi	ぶ bu	べ be	ぼ bo

After six years of elementary school, Japanese children attend three years of junior high school. Many junior high school uniforms consist of a black or navy sailor suit for girls and a military-style uniform for boys. Senior high school consists of three years of study.

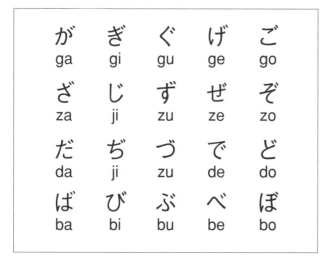

ONE-CIRCLE HIRAGANA CHART

The circle used on the upper right-hand corner of the symbol is called a まる or だくおん. When a まる is added to は, ひ, ふ, へ or ほ, the pronunciation changes.

ぱ pa	ぴ pi	ぷ pu	ぺ pe	ぽ po

かっぱ is a mythical water imp found in swamps and ponds. If the かっぱ spills the water from the plate on its head then it loses all its special powers. かっぱ is a mischievous creature.

SHORT AND LONG VOWELS

The short vowel is written with only one symbol, whereas the long vowel requires two symbols. The long vowel is written by writing the extra required vowel symbol. Note that the long vowel forms for え and お can be written in two ways.

SHORT VOWELS	LONG VOWELS
あ	ああ
い	いい
う	うう
え	えい
	ええ
お	おう
	おお

れんしゅう

| お | ば | あ | さ | ん |

| お | じ | い | さ | ん |

| ふ | う | せ | ん |

| と | け | い |

| お | ね | え | さ | ん |

| す | も | う |

| お | お | き | い |

DOUBLE CONSONANTS

To write a double consonant, write a small っ before the consonant to be doubled.

れんしゅう

| き | っ | さ | て | ん |

A きっさてん is a coffee shop where you can relax with your friends over a cup of freshly-brewed coffee, tea or maybe a soft drink. Prices are very expensive but then you can stay as long as you like.

JAPANESE NUMBERS 1-5

COUNTING THE JAPANESE WAY
This is how the Japanese count from 1 to 5 using their hands. Try it!

JAPANESE NUMBERS 6-10

 六
ろく

七
しち／なな

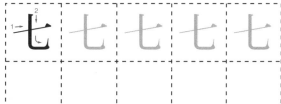

八
はち

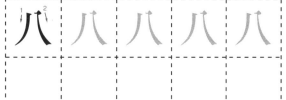

九
きゅう／く

十
じゅう

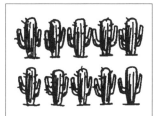

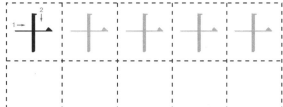

じゃんけん GAME

Westerners often toss a coin to decide the winner of a game. Japanese children play じゃんけん. This game requires two players who simultaneously shake their hands and form either scissors, stone or paper. The winner between scissors and paper—scissors (scissors can cut paper). The winner between stone and scissors—stone (scissors cannot cut a stone). The winner between stone and paper—paper (paper can wrap around a stone).

HIRAGANA SNAP GAME

You will need: One set of hiragana cards per group (2-4 people)

Directions:

一 Form groups and spread the hiragana cards out on the floor. Sit in a circle around them.
二 Have your teacher or class leader call out the hiragana one by one.
三 As you hear the hiragana called, choose the card from the set that correctly matches the sound that is called.
四 You have only one chance to choose the correct card. Your teacher will hold up the card so that you can check if you are correct or not.
五 As you near the end of the game, everyone must put their hands on their heads to make the game a little harder.
六 The winner will be the person with the most cards.
七 If you have more than one winner, play じゃんけん to decide the ultimate winner.

PLAYGROUND HIRAGANA SNAP GAME

You will need: 46 pieces of cardboard and a black oil pen.

Directions:

一 Make up 46 GIANT-size hiragana cards.
二 Go to the school playground and place the cards on the ground.
三 Students must all stand behind a line and run towards the card that is called. Your teacher or class leader can call out the hiragana in a loud voice, or use a microphone.
四 As the whole class can play the game, you will need a scorer.
五 The winner is the person with the most points.

ALL ABOUT ME

Fill in the blanks with information about yourself.

なまえは＿＿＿＿です。

しんちょうは＿＿＿＿せんちです。

＿＿＿＿さいです。

かぞくは＿＿＿＿にんいます。

めが＿＿＿＿です。

かみのけは＿＿＿＿です。

でんわばんごうは＿＿＿＿です。

いちばんすきなともだちは＿＿＿＿です。

すきなかずは＿＿＿＿です。

いちばんすきなたべものは＿＿＿＿です。

なまえは
なんですか。

すきなかずは
なんですか。

HIRAGANA CROSSWORD

Answer the questions in ひらがな.

1					2	■	■		3			4
■	■	■		5			■	■	■	
■	6					■		7		8	
■		■	■	■	■	9		■	■		■
10								■			■
■	■	■	■	■		■	■			■
11		12				■	13			
■	■		■	■	14				■
■	15	16		■	■		■		
■	■	■		■	17			■	

よこ
1. Flamboyant street performers who call out events.
3. A personal seal used instead of a signature.
5. Flown on New Year's Day.
6. Knights of old Japan.
7. Underground railways.
10. Title of this book.
11. Cats that beckon passing customers.
14. Martial art based on samurai sword fighting.
15. Minature ivory carvings.
17. Japanese health food.

たて
2. Meals on wheels.
4. Heated electric table.
6. Cherry blossoms.
8. A charm for good weather.
9. Japanese kids have been playing this since the twelfth century.
10. Festival held on March 3rd.
12. Animals who possess special powers and bewitch people.
13. Public baths.
16. 30-40% of Japan's annual rain falls during this period.